# Mister Magoo Two

(U P A) *Pictures, Inc.*

## SCHOLASTIC BOOK SERVICES

NEW YORK • TORONTO • LONDON • AUCKLAND • SYDNEY • TOKYO

ISBN 0-590-31300-2

Many of the cartoons in this book also appear in THE NEAR-SIGHTED MR. MAGOO.

12 11 10 9 8 7 6 5 4 3 2 1     11     0 1 2 3 4 5/8
Printed in the U.S.A.
01

**HENRY G. SAPERSTEIN ENTERPRISES'**

# THE NEARSIGHTED Mister Magoo

includes Mr. Magoo's adventures
with his nephew, Waldo, and his
loyal servant, Charlie. Charlie
is always polite and helpful,
no matter what weird situations
nearsighted Mr. Magoo gets into.

A Henry G. Saperstein presentation

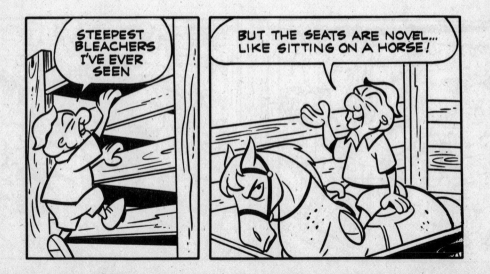